THE GINGERBREAD MAN

Once upon a time a little old (woman) and a little old (man) lived together in a little old (house) in the country. Their children were grown up and had homes of their own and they had only their (cat) to keep them company. Sometimes the  and the  were very lonely. So one day while she was baking, the  decided to make a little  out of gingerbread.

She rolled out the dough and cut it in the shape of a little . She gave

him currants for  , raisins

for  , and red sugar for

his mouth. Then she called

the  to see the  ,
and she put the pan into
the oven to bake.

   Then the and the
sat down together to wait
until the little should
be done.

   When she thought he was
ready, the little opened

the oven door. With a hop

and a skip and a jump, the

 leaped to the floor.

Out of the 🏠 he ran, and down the road, and as he ran he called back over his shoulder, "Run, run, as fast as you can. You can't catch me, I'm a 🍪."

The 👨 ran after the 🍪, and the 👵 ran after the 🍪, and even the 🐱 ran

after the  , but they could

not catch him and the

ran on and on.

Soon the little  saw a  eating grass in the meadow and the  said, "Not so fast,  . I want to eat you."

The  answered, "I've run away from a  and a , and a  and I can run away from you too, I can!"

And the  skipped down the road calling back over his shoulder as he ran, "Run, run, as fast as you can, you can't catch me, I'm a .

The couldn't catch him.

They all followed him, the and the and the and the ; and the

 ran merrily on ahead until he came to a  with a  looking out over the  "Not so fast, little ," said the . "I want to eat you."

The  only ran faster, and as he ran he called out, "I've run away from a , a , a , a , and I

can run away from you too, I

can.'' And he skipped merrily

along singing, ''Run, run, as

fast as you can, you can't catch me, I'm a  ."

They all ran after him, but they could not catch the . Soon they came to a field with a in it and the called out:

"Stop, little ! Stop! I want to eat you."

The little  only ran the faster, and as he ran he called out over his shoulder:

"I've run away from a [old woman], a [man with hat], a [cat], a [cow], a [horse], and I can run away from you too, I can, I can."

They all ran after the  but they could not catch him.

Soon the  came to a field where some were

raking hay, and the

called out, "Stop, little  .
We want to eat you."

The  ran faster than ever.

"I've run away from a  ,
a , a , a , a , a
 ,and I can run away from
you, I can, I can."

And the  skipped merrily

along singing, "Run, run, as

fast as you can. You can't
catch me, I'm a  ."
And they couldn't catch him.

After a while the  saw

a 🦊 leaning against the

stump of a 🌳, and the

said quickly, "I've run away

from a 👵, a 👨, a 🐱,

a 🐮, a 🐴, a 🐷, and a

field full of 🧙, and I can run

away from you too, I can."

The 🦊 laughed. "I don't

want to catch you, little . Why do you run?"

The was so surprised that

he stopped running and they
went on together until they
came to a wide stream.

"Just jump up on my back,"
said the 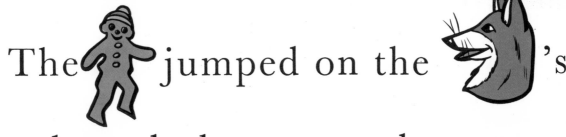. "I will help you
across the water."

The jumped on the 's
back and they started across
the stream. Soon the water

got deeper. "Get up on my

shoulders," said the  .

Again the water got deeper,